1 book
4 readers
2 enjoy!

aRHYTHMetic

Kari-Lynn Winters

poetry by:
Tiffany Stone, Kari-Lynn Winters
& Lori Sherritt-Fleming
artwork by: Scot Ritchie

D1445053

This book was printed in the USA on acid free
paper that contains no fiber from old growth forests,
using ink that is safe for children.

gumboot books
www.gumbootbooks.ca

poetry
aRHYTHMetic © 2009 by Tiffany Stone
Teacup Pups © 2009 by Kari-Lynn Winters
Third in the Herd © 2009 by Tiffany Stone
The Shape of Things © 2009 by Kari-Lynn Winters
Rot-TEN Dragons © 2009 by Lori Sherritt-Fleming
Princess Estimation © 2009 by Tiffany Stone
Kitty Chat © 2009 by Kari-Lynn Winters

artwork
artwork © 2009 by Scot Ritchie

English Version
ISBN 978-0-9784351-5-8

French Version / en français
ISBN 978-0-9784351-7-2

Curriculum Guide: aRHYTHMetic in the Classroom
978-0-9784351-8-9

Note for Librarians

A cataloguing record for this title is available from
Library and Archives Canada at
www.collectionscanada.ca/amicus/index-e.html.

Gumboot Books is a socially and environmentally responsible company. We measure our success by the impact we have on the lives and dreams of our authors and illustrators, the impact we have on the environment, and the ways in which we help to enrich the lives of everyone who reads our books.

If you would like to see how we are reducing our ecological footprint, and how we are supporting community numeracy and literacy projects, please visit us online.

www.gumbootbooks.ca

ORDERING INFORMATION

All of our products are available through Amazon.com, Amazon.ca and other online retailers, or directly from Gumboot Books.

Quantity discounts are available on bulk purchases of this book for resale, educational purposes, subscription incentives, or fundraising initiatives.

For more information, or to place an order, please visit us online at **www.gumbootbooks.ca**

or call 1-888-803-4861 (toll-free from anywhere in North America).

* **Look for our curriculum guide and *aRHYTHMetic* en français!**

* **Did you know that there is an *aRHYTHMetic* stage show? See www.tickletrunkplayers.com for more information.**

* **Tiffany, Kari-Lynn and Lori do school visits. Check out their author websites for details!**

For Carman and the kids —
all number one in my herd. T.S.

For Jonah, Liam, McKenna and all my writing pals—thanks
for helping me shape these snappy, happy poems. K.L.W.

For Dad, Mom, Mike, their family clans and
associated troupes of "Rot-TEN Dragons." L.S.F.

For my grade 2 teacher,
Mrs. Baxter—you're the best. S.R.

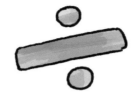

aRHYTHMetic

arithmetic. arithmetic.
a rhythm. a rhythm.
arithmetic. arithmetic.
a rhyme. a rhyme.
arithmetic. arithmetic.
add rhythm. add rhyme.
a-RHYTHM-etic. aRHYTHMetic.
aRHYTHMetic time!

Teacup Pups

Two biscuits for Poodle.
Four for Pug.
Beagle has six,
tucked under the rug.
Eight for Yorkie.
She yaps with glee.
Ten for Whippet.
Time for tea!

Third in the Herd

I'm third in the herd
and I'm proud of it.
Third in the herd
is a perfect fit.

One cow, two cows,
three—that's me.
Third in the herd's
where I want to be.

I'm not second.
I'm not first.
First in the herd
I've heard is the worst.

First through the muck
on a wild, wet day.
First in the herd
has to lead the way.

I'm not first.
I'm not last.
Last in the herd is...
well, she's last.

Last to the pasture,
last into bed.
Last to get water,
last to get fed.

THE SHAPE OF THINGS

Find them all.
Name and compare.
2-D shapes are everywhere.

In the wild.
Hey, why not?
Triangle tooth
and **trapezoid** spot.

Up in trees.
To enjoy.
Hexagon treat
and **rhombus** toy.

Undersea.
There they are.
Oval shell
and five-point **star**.

At the farm.
In disguise.
Circle snout
and **rectangle** eyes.

This shape here.
That shape there.
2-D shapes are everywhere!

Rot-TEN Dragons!

If you look v-e-r-y closely,
when they think you've left home,
you can count rot-TEN dragons
that sneak out to roam.

Count them forwards
and backwards.
In groups of ten they play.
They're coming now.
They're moving fast!
Get out of their way!

TEN slide through the drainpipe,
squooshing through the slime.
All at once they shout out,
"It's P-A-R-T-Y time!"

Swimming in the toilet,
splashing in the tub,
TWENTY dragons sweetly sing,
"Rub-a-dub-scrub!"

Hockey in the hallway,
scraping up the floor,
THIRTY dragon players
shoot and score!

Stomping through the front room,
jumping on the couch,
FORTY dragons somersault
and breathe fire—ouch!

Messing in the kitchen,
playing with the food,
FIFTY dragons sizzle
recipes quite crude!

Hanging from the ceiling,
swinging from the drapes,
SIXTY dragon heroes
swoosh in their capes!

Clowning in the bedroom,
bouncing off the walls,
SEVENTY dragon jugglers
toss colored balls!

Racing through the office,
riding scooter bikes,
EIGHTY dragon grannies
zoom past—yikes!

Drumming in the attic,
playing extra loud,
NINETY dragon rock stars
entertain the crowd!

Spying from the rooftop,
peering left and right,
ONE HUNDRED dragon sentries
gaze through the night!

"People are coming!"
they snort and they hack.
Then ONE HUNDRED dragons
signal to clean up the shack!

NINETY dragon rock stars
finish their last set.

EIGHTY dragon grannies
pack up their wheels and jet.

SEVENTY dragons scuttle
to end their circus play.

**SIXTY dragon heroes
call it a day.**

**FIFTY flambéed dragons
wash each and every cup.**

**FORTY bouncing dragons
stop to clean things up.**

THIRTY hockey dragons
stash away their gear.

TWENTY soggy dragons
mop, shout and cheer.

TEN gooey dragons
halt in mid-glide.

Every rot-TEN dragon
manages to hide!

As your parents enter,
you tell them what you saw.
"Dragons in the house?" they laugh
and look at you in awe.

"Look v-e-r-y closely.
You can count them all in tens."
And you point out secret places
where dragons make their dens.

Princess Estimation

Old King Counting gave his niece,
young Princess Estimation,
a polka-dotted doggy for
her birthday celebration.

"Gee, Uncle, thanks. How simply swell.
My very own Dalmatian!
Oh pretty please, count all her spots.
That's vital information!"

But Uncle had to leave to give
a fencing demonstration.
So Princess did what she does best
and made an estimation.

She picked a patch upon her pup,
and with great concentration,
counted spots in that one patch,
then using speculation,
she guessed how many patches on
the whole of her Dalmatian.

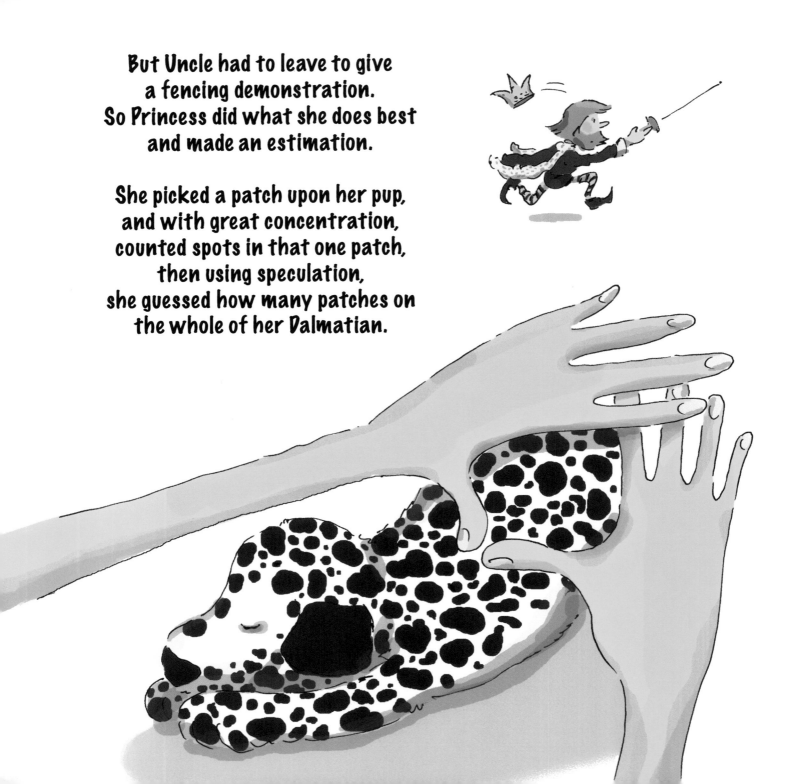

Spots times patches gave the girl
a good approximation
of what a dotty dog she had—
spottiest in the nation!

Kitty Chat

Twelve treats for Chantilly,
who never acts silly
when she is hosting a party.

Burmese eats fourteen,
then licks his fur clean.
(He likes to look like a smartie.)

And in struts Bombay,
who has plenty to say.
He gobbles down sixteen more.

Eighteen for Korat,
a hardy little cat.
She sneaks hers out the door.

Then Havana Brown,
the sleekest in town,
mews, "I think you've all had plenty."

She prowls to the table,
and best as she's able,
scoffs down the final twenty.

about Tiffany Stone

www.TiFFanyStone.ca

Tiffany Stone is primarily a children's poet-although she has written 1 non-fiction book: Tall Tale: The True Story of the World's Largest Tin Soldier (Wright Publications). Her 2 collections of poetry for kids are Floyd the Flamingo and His Flock of Friends and Baaaad Animals, both published by Tradewind Books. She also writes poems for KNOW: The Science Magazine for Curious Kids. Tiffany lives in Maple Ridge, BC with her 3 children and 4 cats.

about Kari-Lynn Winters

www.Kariwinters.com

At Lynhurst Elementary in Ontario, Kari-Lynn was dreadful at math, and her poetry wasn't very good, either. Her best subject was recess, because she could act out all of her funny stories with her friends. Today, Kari-Lynn lives in Vancouver, BC with her husband, 2 children, and 2 cats. She continues to tell stories and act them out with her friends. Kari-Lynn writes for and performs with a local children's theater troupe called The Tickle Trunk Players. aRHYTHMetic is Kari-Lynn's second picture book. Soaring to shelves this fall (2009) is When Chickens Fly (Gumboot Books).

ABOUT LORI SHERRITT-FLEMING

www.LORISHERRITT.COM

As a stilt walker and "circus engineer," clowning around comes naturally to Lori. She loves to play with words, especially ones that leap from the page to the stage with her company, The Tickle Trunk Players. To support all of this fun, Lori serves as the BC Regional Manager for the Royal Conservatory's Learning Through the Arts program where, as a mentor artist, she regularly facilitates teacher professional development workshops that infuse curriculum with creativity and fun. aRHYTHMetic is Lori's first book.

ABOUT SCOT RITCHIE

www.SCOTRITCHIE.COM

Scot Ritchie is a Canadian author and illustrator. Working freelance, he has had the opportunity to do everything from children's literature to advertising to posters and educational material. His work can be found in publications including: Wall St. Journal, Newsweek, Chicago Tribune, New York Magazine and Reader's Digest. His 40+ children's books have been translated into Korean, Dutch, French and Polish.

9 780978 435158